Oct 10, 2017

Tara,

I hope you can
use this at school!

Love
Liz Adelman

An American Independence Day Riddle:

I WAS BORN ON JULY 4, 1776,

WHEN THE THIRTEEN AMERICAN
COLONIES DECLARED THEIR
INDEPENDENCE FROM ENGLAND.
ON THAT 4TH OF JULY, AND ALL SINCE,
AMERICANS COAST TO COAST
WATCH FIREWORKS DISPLAYS
TO CELEBRATE MY BIRTHDAY!

WHO AM I?

Answer: The United States of America (U.S.A.)

FUN U.S. TRIVIA: Who is "Uncle Sam"?

On September 7, 1813, a Troy, New York meat packer named Samuel Wilson stamped "U.S." for "United States" on barrels of meat sent to soldiers during the War of 1812. A local newspaper reported that the barrels of meat were said to be from "Uncle Sam" and the nickname for the abbreviation "U.S." was born. Cartoonist Thomas Nast first gave an identity to Uncle Sam, portraying him as a white-bearded old man dressed in stars and stripes.

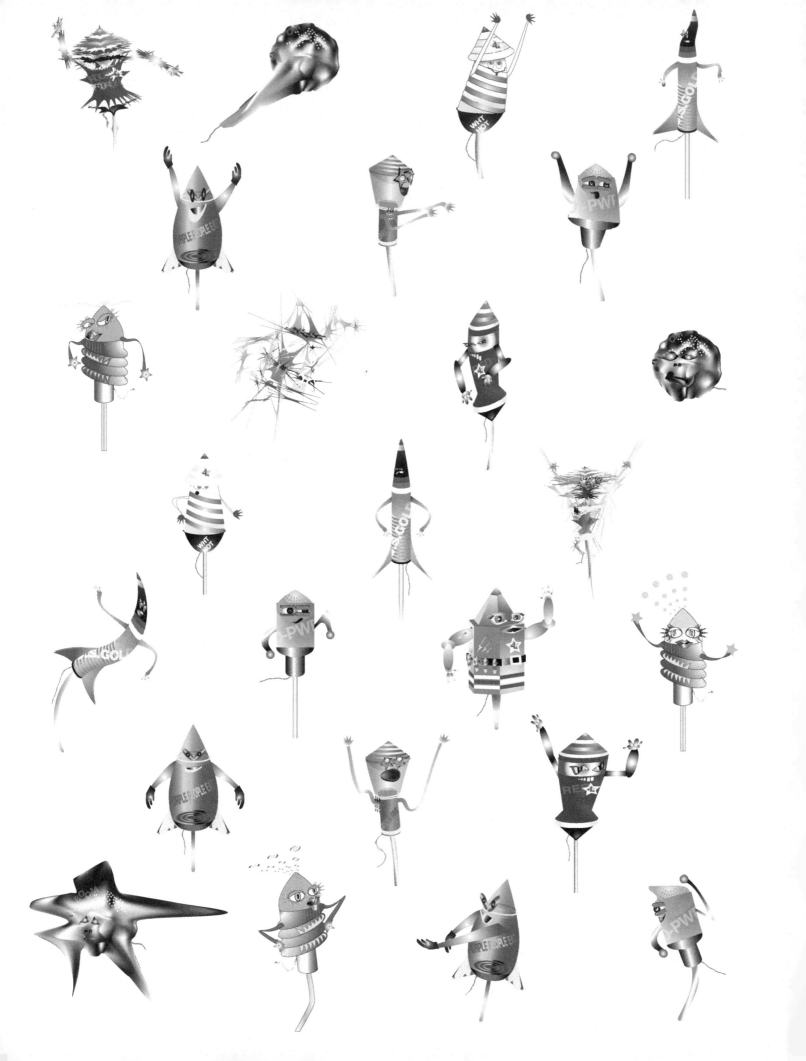

KaBOOM!

A 4th of July Story

Published by Graphocity Books
Naperville, Illinois
www.graphocity.com

All inquiries should be addressed to Graphocity, 1087 Pomona Ct., Naperville, IL 60540.

ISBN number: 978-1-946924-00-1

Library of Congress Control Number: 2017903518

First Edition

For

Austin, Peyton, Logan, Fiona and Dylan

THE **4TH OF JULY** dawned sunny and bright.

The fireworks began **PLANNING THE SHOW** for that night.

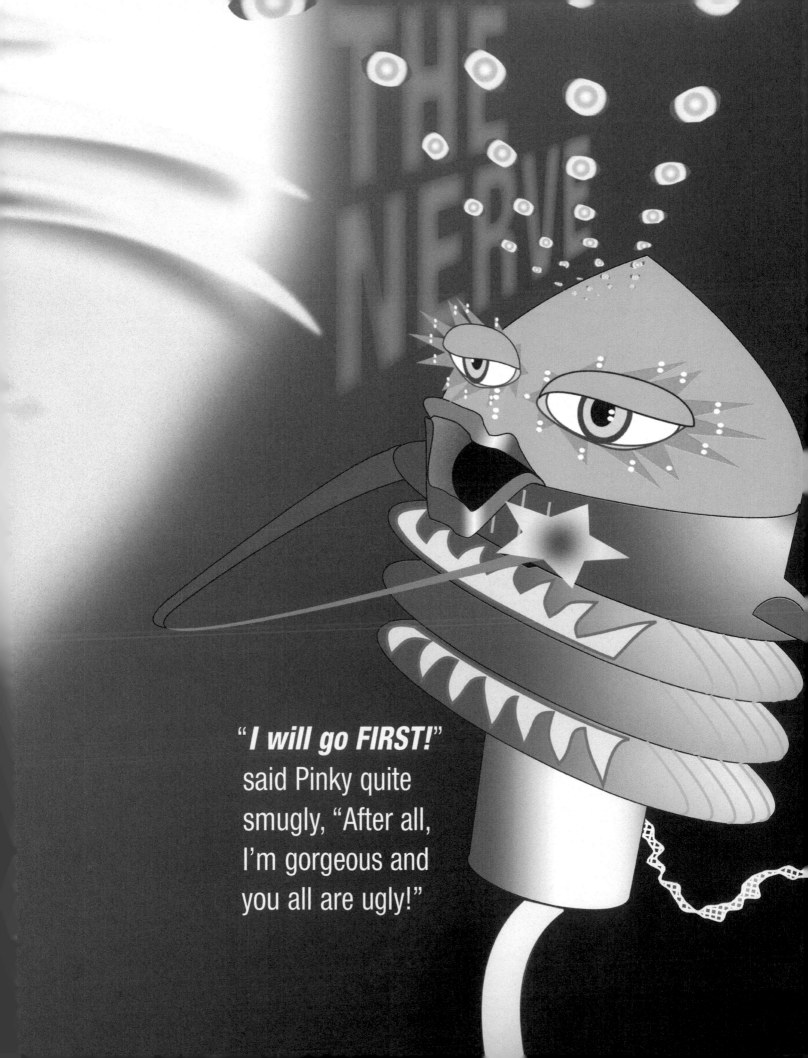

"We'll fill in the **MIDDLE**," cried Purple and Green, "with a dazzling display, the best ever seen!"

"Night's **EDGES**
need us," exclaimed
Orange and Gold,
"We'll brighten night's
darkness to a daylight bold!"

"And then," blasted Blue, with all he could muster, "Red, White and I will plan an **END-OF-SHOW BUSTER!**"

"I know when I'll go," shouted KaBOOM, "I'll sneak in the show **WHEREVER THERE'S ROOM!**"

Strained firework **SILENCE** met KaBOOM's remark. Then Purple pushed forward— ***"YOU'RE BANNED FROM THE PARK!"***

"People **DON'T WANT YOU** on fireworks night because when you explode, you give them **SUCH FRIGHT!**"

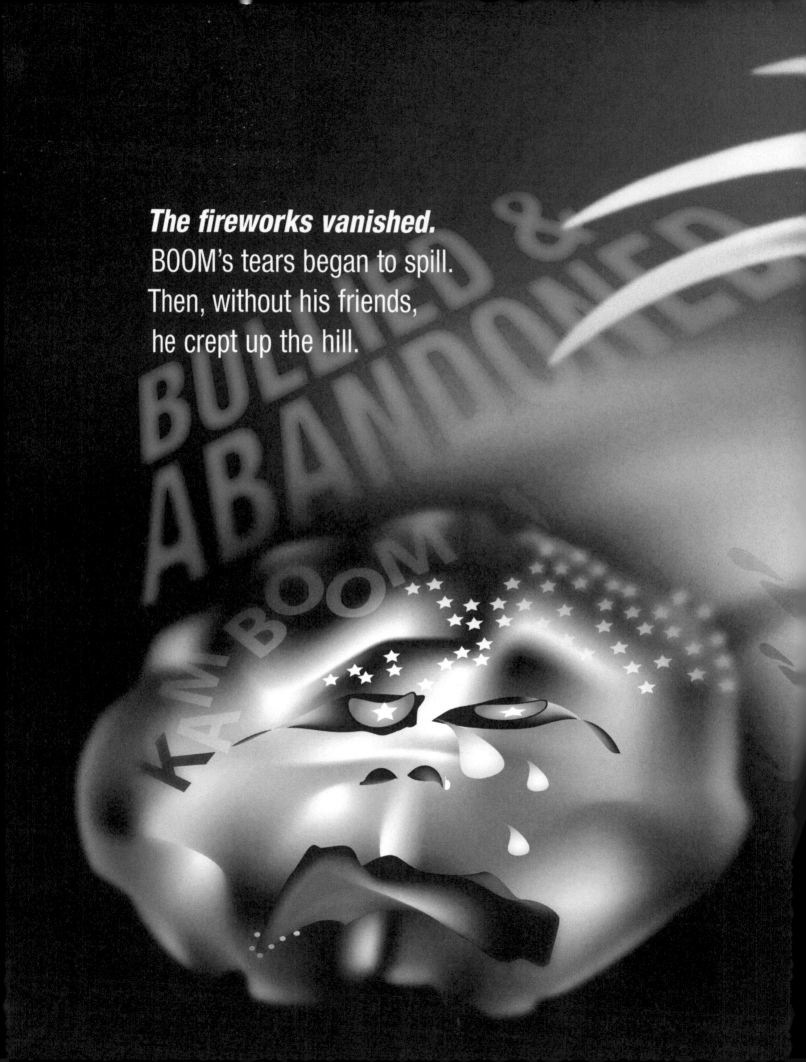

The fireworks vanished.
BOOM's tears began to spill.
Then, without his friends,
he crept up the hill.

Meanwhile…
THE TOWNSFOLK
GATHERED down at the
park for pre-show music
and a speech by Mayor Clark.

When the Mayor's speech
ended and the music stopped,
**Pinky LET LOOSE
and all eyes POPPED!**

The fireworks sparkled
on the canvas of night,
bursting bright colors
WITH ALL OF THEIR MIGHT!

For thirty packed minutes the fireworks paraded, while the audience *OOOOHHH'D, AWWWWHH'D AND APPLAUDED!*

Then Red, White and Blue
concluded the show with a
non-stop fountain of
PATRIOTIC GLOW!

At the end of the show,
the fireworks expected
CHEERS from the crowd,
for the show they'd perfected.
But, instead of cheers,
all they heard was *A MURMUR.*
Then, old folks and young
COMPLAINED WITH A FERVOR!

The crowd's unrest grew as the fireworks worried.
Then, out of the mob, a dark figure hurried!
KaBOOM!

pop!

"**I HOPE I CAN HELP**. I'll certainly try." And above angry faces, KaBOOM started to fly! He gave a little POP to quiet the crowd. Then BOOM's **KA-BOOM** made the crowd gasp aloud!

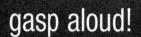

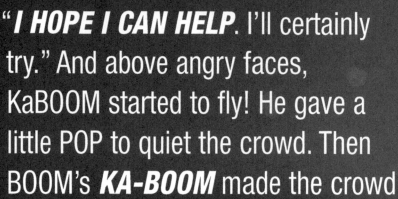

As BOOM's thunder **RESOUNDED,** the boys covered their ears, girls fell to their knees and moms wiped baby tears!

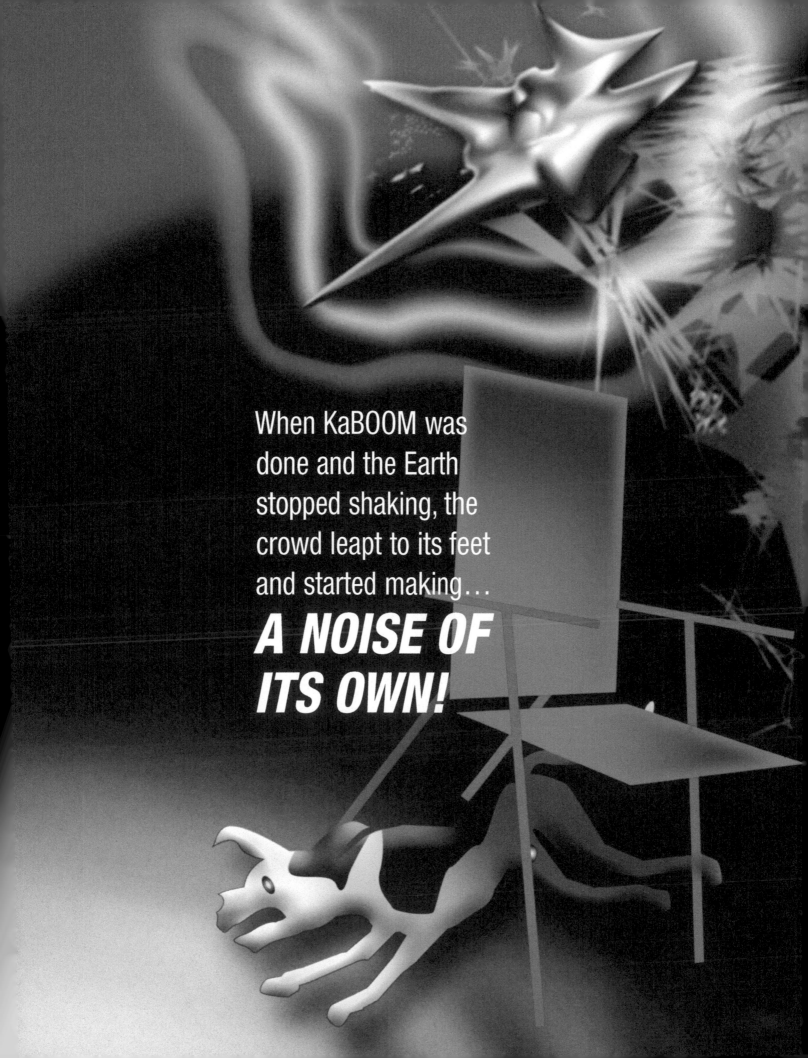

When KaBOOM was done and the Earth stopped shaking, the crowd leapt to its feet and started making…

A NOISE OF ITS OWN!

"YEEEEEAAAAAAA!"
they shouted.

"Thank you, KaBOOM,
for the **POW, PUMF** and **BAM,**
It's the **LOUDEST** 4th ever!

"Happy Birthday,
UNCLE SAM!"

The First July 4th Celebration

Article as it appeared in the *Virginia Gazette*, July 18, 1777

Original Page as Printed in the
Virginia Gazette: Purdie, July 18, 1777,
Celebration Story Highlighted

Yesterday the 4th of July, being the Anniversary of the Independence of the United States of America, was celebrated in this city with demonstration of joy and festivity. About noon all the armed ships and gallies in the river were drawn up before the city, dressed in the gayest manner, with the colours of the United States and streamers displayed. At one o'clock, the yards being properly manned, they began the celebration of the day by a discharge of thirteen cannon from each of the ships, and one from each of the thirteen gallies, in honour of the Thirteen United States. In the afternoon an elegant dinner was prepared for Congress, to which were invited the President and Supreme Executive Council, and Speaker of the Assembly of this State, the General Officers and Colonels of the army, and strangers of eminence, and the members of the several Continental Boards in town. The Hessian band of music taken in Trenton the 26th of December last, attended and heightened the festivity

with some fine performances suited to the joyous occasion, while a corps of British deserters, taken into the service of the continent by the State of Georgia, being drawn up before the door, filled up the intervals with feux de joie. After dinner a number of toasts were drank, all breaking independence, and a generous love of liberty, and commemorating the memories of those brave and worthy patriots who gallantly exposed their lives, and fell gloriously in defence [sic] of freedom and the righteous cause of their country. Each toasts was followed by a discharge of artillery and small arms, and a suitable piece of music by the Hessian band. The glorious fourth of July was reiterated three times accompanied with triple discharges of cannon and small arms, and loud huzzas that resounded from street to street through the city. Towards evening several troops of horse, a corps of artillery, and a brigade of North Carolina forces, which was in town on its way to join the grand army, were drawn up in Second street and reviewed by Congress and the General Officers. The evening was closed with the ringing of bells, and at night there was a grand exhibition of fireworks, which began and concluded with thirteen rockets on the commons, and the city was beautifully illuminated. Every thing was conducted with the greatest order and decorum, and the face of joy and gladness was universal. Thus may the 4th of July, that glorious and ever memorable day, be celebrated through America, by the sons of freedom, from age to age till time shall be no more. Amen, and amen.

The Declaration of Independence

Final Version adopted by the Second Continental Congress on July 4, 1776

After years of oppression, armed conflict between American Freedom Fighters and British soldiers broke out in April, 1775. It would be fifteen months until the Thirteen American Colonies declared their independence from Great Britain.

Declaration of Independence IN CONGRESS, July 4, 1776. The unanimous Declaration of the thirteen united States of America, When in the Course of human events, it becomes necessary for one people to dissolve the political bands which have connected them with another, and to assume among the powers of the earth, the separate and equal station to which the Laws of Nature and of Nature's God entitle them, a decent respect to the opinions of mankind requires that they should declare the causes which impel them to the separation.

We hold these truths to be self-evident, that all men are created equal, that they are endowed by their Creator with certain unalienable Rights, that among these are Life, Liberty and the pursuit of Happiness.—That to secure these rights, Governments are instituted among Men, deriving their just powers from

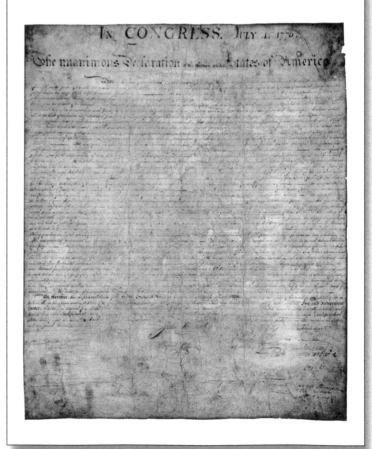

The Original Declaration of Independence Document Is now Displayed in the Rotunda of the National Archives Building in Washington, DC

the consent of the governed,—That whenever any Form of Government becomes destructive of these ends, it is the Right of the People to alter or to abolish it, and to institute new Government, laying its foundation on such principles and organizing its powers in such form, as to them shall seem most likely to effect their Safety and Happiness. Prudence, indeed, will dictate that Governments long established should not be changed for light and transient causes; and accordingly all experience hath shewn, that mankind are more disposed to suffer, while evils are sufferable, than to right themselves by abolishing the forms to which they are accustomed. But when a long train of abuses and usurpations, pursuing invariably the same Object evinces a design to reduce them under absolute Despotism, it is their right, it is their duty, to throw off such Government, and to provide new Guards for their future security.—Such has been the patient sufferance of these Colonies; and such is now the necessity which constrains them to alter their former Systems of Government. The history of the present

King of Great Britain is a history of repeated injuries and usurpations, all having in direct object the establishment of an absolute Tyranny over these States. To prove this, let Facts be submitted to a candid world.

He has refused his Assent to Laws, the most wholesome and necessary for the public good.

He has forbidden his Governors to pass Laws of immediate and pressing importance, unless suspended in their operation till his Assent should be obtained; and when so suspended, he has utterly neglected to attend to them.

He has refused to pass other Laws for the accommodation of large districts of people, unless those people would relinquish the right of Representation in the Legislature, a right inestimable to them and formidable to tyrants only.

He has called together legislative bodies at places unusual, uncomfortable, and distant from the depository of their public Records, for the sole purpose of fatiguing them into compliance with his measures.

He has dissolved Representative Houses repeatedly, for opposing with

manly firmness his invasions on the rights of the people.

He has refused for a long time, after such dissolutions, to cause others to be elected; whereby the Legislative powers, incapable of Annihilation, have returned to the People at large for their exercise; the State remaining in the mean time exposed to all the dangers of invasion from without, and convulsions within.

He has endeavoured to prevent the population of these States; for that purpose obstructing the Laws for Naturalization of Foreigners; refusing to pass others to encourage their migrations hither, and raising the conditions of new Appropriations of Lands.

He has obstructed the Administration of Justice, by refusing his Assent to Laws for establishing Judiciary powers.

He has made Judges dependent on his Will alone, for the tenure of their offices, and the amount and payment of their salaries.

He has erected a multitude of New Offices, and sent hither swarms of Officers to harrass our people, and eat out their substance.

He has kept among us, in times of peace, Standing Armies without the Consent of our legislatures.

He has affected to render the Military independent of and superior to the Civil power.

He has combined with others to subject us to a jurisdiction foreign to our constitution, and unacknowledged by our laws; giving his Assent to their Acts of pretended Legislation:

For Quartering large bodies of armed troops among us:

For protecting them, by a mock Trial, from punishment for any Murders which they should commit on the Inhabitants of these States:

For cutting off our Trade with all parts of the world:

For imposing Taxes on us without our Consent:

For depriving us in many cases, of the benefits of Trial by Jury:

For transporting us beyond Seas to be tried for pretended offences

For abolishing the free System of English Laws in a neighbouring Province, establishing therein an Arbitrary government, and enlarging

its Boundaries so as to render it at once an example and fit instrument for introducing the same absolute rule into these Colonies:

For taking away our Charters, abolishing our most valuable Laws, and altering fundamentally the Forms of our Governments:

For suspending our own Legislatures, and declaring themselves invested with power to legislate for us in all cases whatsoever.

He has abdicated Government here, by declaring us out of his Protection and waging War against us.

He has plundered our seas, ravaged our Coasts, burnt our towns, and destroyed the lives of our people.

He is at this time transporting large Armies of foreign Mercenaries to compleat the works of death, desolation and tyranny, already begun with circumstances of Cruelty & perfidy scarcely paralleled in the most barbarous ages, and totally unworthy of the Head of a civilized nation.He has constrained our fellow Citizens taken Captive on the high Seas to bear Arms against their Country, to become the executioners of their friends and Brethren, or to fall themselves by their Hands.

He has excited domestic insurrections amongst us, and has endeavoured to bring on the inhabitants of our frontiers, the merciless Indian Savages, whose known rule of warfare, is an undistinguished destruction of all ages, sexes and conditions.

In every stage of these Oppressions We have Petitioned for Redress in the most humble terms: Our repeated Petitions have been answered only by repeated injury. A Prince whose character is thus marked by every act which may define a Tyrant, is unfit to be the ruler of a free people. Nor have We been wanting in attentions to our Brittish brethren. We have warned them from time to time of attempts by their legislature to extend an unwarrantable jurisdiction over us. We have reminded them of the circumstances of our emigration and settlement here. We have appealed to their native justice and magnanimity, and we have conjured them by the ties of our common kindred to disavow these usurpations,

which, would inevitably interrupt our connections and correspondence. They too have been deaf to the voice of justice and of consanguinity. We must, therefore, acquiesce in the necessity, which denounces our Separation, and hold them, as we hold the rest of mankind, Enemies in War, in Peace Friends.

We, therefore, the Representatives of the united States of America, in General Congress, Assembled, appealing to the Supreme Judge of the world for the rectitude of our intentions, do, in the Name, and by Authority of the good People of these Colonies, solemnly publish and declare, That these United Colonies are, and of Right ought to be Free and Independent States; that they are Absolved from all Allegiance to the British Crown, and that all political connection between them and the State of Great Britain, is and ought to be totally dissolved; and that as Free and Independent States, they have full Power to levy War, conclude Peace, contract Alliances, establish Commerce, and to do all other Acts and Things which

Independent States may of right do. And for the support of this Declaration, with a firm reliance on the protection of divine Providence, we mutually pledge to each other our Lives, our Fortunes and our sacred Honor.

SIGNATURES:
John Hancock,
President
Attested,
Charles Thomson,
Secretary

NEW HAMPSHIRE
Josiah Bartlett
William Whipple
Matthew Thornton

MASSACHUSETTS
Samuel Adams
John Adams
Robert Treat Paine
Elbridge Gerry

RHODE ISLAND
Stephen Hopkins
William Ellery

CONNECTICUT
Roger Sherman
Samuel Huntington
William Williams
Oliver Wolcott

GEORGIA
Button Gwinnett
Lyman Hall
George Walton

MARYLAND
Samuel Chase
William Paca
Thomas Stone
Charles Carroll of Carrollton

VIRGINIA
George Wythe
Richard Henry Lee
Thomas Jefferson
Benjamin Harrison
Thomas Nelson, Jr.
Francis Lightfoot Lee
Carter Braxton

NEW YORK
William Floyd
Philip Livingston
Francis Lewis
Lewis Morris

PENNSYLVANIA
Robert Morris
Benjamin Rush
Benjamin Franklin
John Morton
George Clymer
James Smith
George Taylor
James Wilson
George Ross

DELAWARE
Caesar Rodney
George Read
Thomas McKean

NORTH CAROLINA
William Hooper
Joseph Hewes
John Penn

SOUTH CAROLINA
Edward Rutledge
Thomas Heyward, Jr.
Thomas Lynch, Jr.
Arthur Middleton

NEW JERSEY
Richard Stockton
John Witherspoon
Francis Hopkinson
John Hart
Abraham Clark

Favorite American Holidays

DATE	NAME	TYPE
Jan 1	New Year's Day	Federal
Jan	Martin Luther King Jr. Day	Federal
Feb 14	Valentines Day	Observance
Feb	Presidents' Day	Federal
Mar	St Patrick's Day	Observance
Mar or Apr	Passover (first day)	Jewish
Apr 16	Easter Sunday	Christian
Varies	Isra and Mi'raj	Muslim
Varies	Ramadan starts	Muslim
May	Memorial Day	Federal
Jul 4	Independence Day	Federal
Varies	Eid al-Adha	Muslim
Sep	Labor Day	Federal
Sep	Rosh Hashana	Jewish
Varies	Muharram	Muslim
Sep	Yom Kippur	Jewish
Oct	Columbus Day	Federal
Oct 31	Halloween	Observance
Nov	Veterans Day	Federal
Nov	Thanksgiving Day	Federal
Varies	The Prophet's Birthday	Muslim
Dec	Chanukah/Hanukkah (first day)	Jewish
Dec 24	Christmas Eve	Christian
Dec 25	Christmas Day	Federal

Acknowledgements

Writing is rewarding but getting a story published can be mind numbing, and publishing with polish requires the eyes of a great editor, like Bobbie Parkhill. Thank you, Bobbie. Publishing with fun and laughter, on the other hand, requires a creative, funny guy, like my publishing-partner and husband, Bruce. Thank you, Bruce (I love you). Thanks, too, to all of you, my friends and family, who have tirelessly read and re-read my stories over the years, making much needed suggestions along the way.

About the Author

Elizabeth (Liz) Bockelman was born in 1955, in the small town of Rochelle, Illinois. She earned a BFA from the University of Illinois at Champaign Urbana. Liz began a graphic design career in 1977 and started her own agency, Graphocity, in 2001. She redirected Graphocity to a publishing company for both books and fine art in 2017. Liz has always loved to write and tell stories to entertain family and friends, especially ones that illustrate a particular idea or moral. She has now added 'author' to her "list of hats," which include daughter, sister, wife, aunt, mom, grandmother and friend, as well as designer, photographer, artist, and songwriter. "I like nothing better than to solve a problem. I hope that I can use the entertainment of the written story to tease, challenge and offer some problem-solving ideas to my readers — and maybe they will send their ideas back to me," says Liz. "You can visit me at lizbockelman.com."

CPSIA information can be obtained
at www.ICGtesting.com
Printed in the USA
LVOW06*0059210417
531591LV00012B/21/P